English text **Alison Winn**

HODDER AND STOUGHTON

LONDON SYDNEY AUCKLAND TORONTO

Gunilla Wolde

Emma's baby brother

Here is Emma's baby brother.
He is very much smaller than Emma.

He has tiny hands, tiny feet,
a tiny little nose like a button.

When he is asleep he is very, very, quiet.

When he is awake he sometimes cries.
Then he is *so* noisy he can be heard
all over the house.

Sometimes when Emma's baby brother cries
Mum comforts and feeds him.

She has special food in her breasts that baby brother enjoys very much. Whenever he cuddles up to Mum he stops crying at once.

Emma doesn't like baby brother very much when Mum is feeding him. She would like to give him away to *another* lady.

Emma wishes she could be a
baby all over again and have
Mum *all* to herself.

When Mum has finished feeding baby brother
Emma is glad she *is* a big girl.
Mum asks her to help to get the things that
baby brother needs for his bath.

She is tall enough – standing on tip toe
to reach the soap, towel, baby oil, nappies and
clean pants from the shelf.
Mum mixes a bowl of cold and warm
water together.

Sometimes when Emma is looking after baby brother
Mum lays him down on a rug
so that he can't fall off anything.
Emma peels off his pants –
and baby brother
giggles happily.

Then she takes off his nappy
which is sopping wet *and*
dirty. Baby brother is
too little to use
his pot yet.

Now Emma's baby brother has his bath.
Mum does this
because dirty babies need
very careful washing
and drying.

It's time now to put on a clean nappy —
and his new stripey pants.
But first Emma smoothes baby oil on his bottom.
This is so he won't get red and sore
when he wets his nappy again.

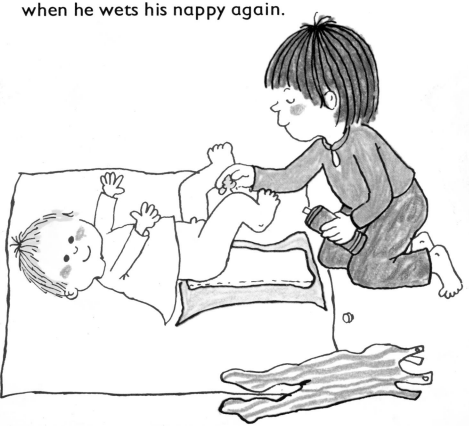

All the time Emma is fixing his nappy and his pants baby brother is wriggling and giggling. Emma thinks that wriggling, giggling, kicking babies are most *difficult* to dress.

Suddenly baby brother grabs a handful of
her hair and tugs very hard.
"Oooh," shrieks Emma —
and tears come in her eyes.

Mum has to rescue her from baby brother's clutches. Babies just love to grab anything and everything with their tiny little fingers.

Now it is time for Emma to eat a nice rosy apple
and for baby brother to have his juice.
He doesn't like it at first – and spits it out.

"It won't be long now,"
says Mum, "before he is
eating with a spoon."

When baby brother sees Emma enjoying her apple he decides he *does* like his juice after all. When it has all gone, he yawns and looks very sleepy.

When he is put into his cot – he cries just a little – but Emma talks quietly to him until he falls asleep.

Emma thinks that baby brothers are funny.
Sometimes – they are a great big nuisance
and sometimes they are lovely and sweet.
Mostly – thinks Emma –
they are lovely
and cuddly and sweet.